Musings on Science

From Pythagoras to Stephen Hawking

Edited by Jude Patterson

BARNES &NOBLE
BOOKS
NEW YORK

The quotes in this book have been drawn from many sources, and are assumed to be accurate as quoted in their previously published forms. Although every effort has been made to verify the quotes and sources, the publisher cannot guarantee their perfect accuracy.

2003 Barnes & Noble Books

ISBN 0-7607-4886-1

Printed and bound in the United States of America

M 9 8 7 6 5 4 3 2 1

What Is Science?

Science is organized knowledge.

—HERBERT SPENCER, *Education,* 1861

Science is the knowledge of Consequences, and dependence of one fact upon another.

—THOMAS HOBBES, *Leviathan,* 1651

Science is built up of facts, as a house is built of stones; but an accumulation of facts is no more a science than a heap of stones is a house.

—HENRI POINCARÉ, *Science and Hypothesis,* 1905

Science is the knowledge of many, orderly and methodically digested and arranged, so as to become attainable by one.

—JOHN HERSCHEL, *A Preliminary Discourse on the Study of Natural Philosophy,* 1830

Science is the attempt to make the chaotic diversity of our sense-experience correspond to a logically uniform system of thought.

—ALBERT EINSTEIN, *Out of My Later Years,* 1950

The aim of science is to apprehend this purely intelligible world as a thing in itself, an object which is what it is independently of all thinking, and thus antithetical to the sensible world.... The world of thought is the universal, the timeless and spaceless, the absolutely necessary, whereas the world of sense is the contingent, the changing and moving appearance which somehow indicates or symbolizes it.

—R. G. COLLINGWOOD (1889-1943)

Everywhere order reigns, so that when some circumstances have been noted we can foresee that others will be present. The progress of science consists in observing these interconnections and in showing with a patient ingenuity that the events of this ever-shifting world are but examples of a few general connections or relations called laws. To see what is general in what is particular and what is permanent in what is transitory is the aim of scientific thought.

—ALFRED NORTH WHITEHEAD,
An Introduction to Mathematics, 1911

Every science has for its basis a system of principles as fixed and unalterable as those by which the universe is regulated and governed. Man cannot make principles; he can only discover them.

—THOMAS PAINE, *The Age of Reason*, 1794

Man is the interpreter of nature, science the right interpretation.

—WILLIAM WHEWELL, *Philosophy of the Inductive Sciences*, 1840

Our ideas must be as broad as Nature if they are to interpret Nature.

—ARTHUR CONAN DOYLE, "A Study in Scarlet," 1888

The "control of nature" is a phrase conceived in arrogance, born of the Neanderthal age of biology and the convenience of man.

—RACHEL CARSON, *Silent Spring,* 1962

In our description of nature the purpose is not to disclose the real essence of the phenomena but only to track down, so far as it is possible, relations between the manifold aspects of our experience.

—NIELS BOHR, *Atomic Theory and the Description of Nature,* 1934

All science is methodology with regard to the Absolute. Therefore, there need be no fear of the unequivocally methodological. It is a husk, but not more than everything except the One.

—FRANZ KAFKA, *The Third Notebook,* entry for 18 October 1917

Science may be described as the art of systematic over-simplification.

—KARL POPPER, in *Observer*, 1 August 1982

Science means simply the aggregate of all the recipes that are always successful. All the rest is literature.

—PAUL VALÉRY, *Moralités*, 1932

The scientific mind does not so much provide the right answers as ask the right questions.

—CLAUDE LÉVI-STRAUSS,
The Raw and the Cooked, 1964

That is the essence of science: ask an impertinent question, and you are on the way to a pertinent answer.

—JACOB BRONOWSKI, *The Ascent of Man,* 1973

No great discovery was ever made in science except by one who lifted his nose above the grindstone of details and ventured on a more comprehensive vision.

—ALBERT EINSTEIN, in Morris R. Cohen,
The Meaning of Human History, 1947

If I have seen further it is by standing on the shoulders of Giants.

—ISAAC NEWTON, letter to Robert Hooke,
5 February 1675/76, referring to his dependence
on the works of Galileo and Kepler

In science men have discovered an activity of the very highest value in which they are no longer, as in art, dependent for progress upon the appearance of continually greater genius, for in science the successors stand upon the shoulders of their predecessors; where one man of supreme genius has invented a method, a thousand lesser men can apply it.

—BERTRAND RUSSELL,
A Free Man's Worship and Other Essays, 1976

One can organize to apply a discovery already made, but not to make one. Only a free individual can make a discovery.... Can you imagine an organization of scientists making the discoveries of Charles Darwin?

—ALBERT EINSTEIN, in *Atlantic,* November 1945

It is the lone worker who makes the first advance in a subject: the details may be worked out by a team, but the prime idea is due to the enterprise, thought and perception of an individual.

—ALEXANDER FLEMING, biochemist who discovered penicillin, address at Edinburgh University, 1951

Among scientists are collectors, classifiers, and compulsive tidiers-up; many are detectives by temperament and many are explorers; some are artists and others artisans. There are poet-scientists and philosopher-scientists and even a few mystics.

—PETER MEDAWAR, *The Art of the Soluble*, 1967

Every science begins as philosophy and ends as art.

—WILL DURANT, *The Story of Philosophy*, 1926

Both the man of science and the man of art live always at the edge of mystery, surrounded by it. Both, as a measure of their creation, have always had to do with the harmonization of what is new with what is familiar, with the balance between novelty and synthesis, with the struggle to make partial order in total chaos.... This cannot be an easy life.

—J. ROBERT OPPENHEIMER (1902-67),
in Robert Jungk, *Brighter Than a Thousand Suns,* 1970

Science begins with the world we have to live in, accepting its data and trying to explain its laws. From there, it moves toward the imagination: it becomes a mental construct, a model of a possible way of interpreting experience. The further it goes in this direction, the more it tends to speak the language of mathematics, which is really one of the languages of the imagination, along with literature and music.

—NORTHROP FRYE, *The Educated Imagination,* 1964

It is impossible to dissociate language from science or science from language, because every natural science always involves three things: the sequence of phenomena on which the science is based; the abstract concepts which call these phenomena to mind; and the words in which the concepts are expressed. To call forth a concept a word is needed; to portray a phenomenon, a concept is needed. All three mirror one and the same reality.

—ANTOINE-LAURENT LAVOISIER,
Traité Elémentaire de Chimie, 1789

Science is spectral analysis. Art is light synthesis.

—KARL KRAUS, satirist, *Pro Domo et Mundo,* 1912

The true artist is quite rational as well as imaginative and knows what he is doing; if he does not, his art suffers. The true scientist is quite imaginative as well as rational, and sometimes leaps to solutions where reason can follow only slowly; if he does not, his science suffers.

—ISAAC ASIMOV, *The Roving Mind,* 1983

If scientific reasoning were limited to the logical processes of arithmetic, we should not get very far in our understanding of the physical world. One might as well attempt to grasp the game of poker entirely by the use of the mathematics of probability.

—VANNEVAR BUSH, *Science Is Not Enough,* 1967

The union of the mathematician with the poet, fervor with measure, passion with correctness, this surely is the ideal.

—WILLIAM JAMES, *Clifford's Lectures and Essays,* 1879

True science investigates and brings to human perception such truths and such knowledge as the people of a given time and society consider most important. Art transmits these truths from the region of perception to the region of emotion.

—LEO TOLSTOY, *What Is Art?,* 1898

Shakespeare would have grasped wave functions, Donne would have understood complementarity and relative time. They would have been excited. What richness! They would have plundered this new science for their imagery. And they would have educated their audiences too.

—IAN MCEWAN, *The Child in Time,* 1987

Language is only the instrument of science, and words are but the signs of ideas: I wish, however, that the instrument might be less apt to decay, and that signs might be permanent, like the things which they denote.

—SAMUEL JOHNSON,
A Dictionary of the English Language, 1755

Scientific truth should be presented in different forms, and should be regarded as equally scientific whether it appears in the robust form and the vivid colouring of a physical illustration, or in the tenuity and paleness of a symbolic expression.

—JAMES CLERK MAXWELL (1831-79, attributed),
in *Physics Teacher,* December 1969

Science can only be created by those who are thoroughly imbued with the aspiration towards truth and understanding. The source of feeling, however, springs from the sphere of religion. To this there also belongs the faith in the possibility that the regulations valid for the world of existence are rational, that is, comprehensible to reason. I cannot conceive of a genuine scientist without that profound faith. The situation may be expressed by an image: Science without religion is lame, religion without science is blind.

—Albert Einstein, *Out of My Later Years,* 1950

True science and true religion are twin sisters, and the separation of either from the other is sure to prove the death of both. Science prospers exactly in proportion as it is religious; and religion flourishes in exact proportion to the scientific depth and firmness of its basis.

—T. H. Huxley, in Herbert Spencer, *Education,* 1861

If [scientists] are worthy of the name, they are indeed about God's path and about his bed and spying out all his ways.

—Samuel Butler (1835-1902), *Notebooks*

Progressively, continuously, and almost simultaneously, religious and scientific concepts are ridding themselves of their coarse and local components, reaching higher and higher levels of abstraction and purity. Both the myths of religion and the laws of science, it is now becoming apparent, are not so much descriptions of facts as symbolic expressions of cosmic truths.

—René Dubos, *A God Within*, 1972

Mathematics,
Queen of the Sciences

If in other sciences we should arrive at certainty without doubt and truth without error, it behoves us to place the foundations of knowledge in mathematics.

—ROGER BACON, *Opus Majus*, 1267

Numerical precision is the very soul of science.

—D'ARCY WENTWORTH THOMPSON, zoologist,
On Growth and Form, 1917

All the mathematical sciences are founded on relations between physical laws and laws of numbers, so that the aim of exact science is to reduce the problems of nature to the determination of quantities by operations with numbers.

—JAMES CLERK MAXWELL,
On Faraday's Lines of Force, 1856

Mathematics is the science which draws necessary conclusions.

—BENJAMIN PEIRCE, *Linear Associative Algebra,* 1870

Mathematics is the queen of the sciences—and number theory is the queen of mathematics.

—CARL FRIEDRICH GAUSS (1777–1855), in Sartorius von Waltershausen, *Gauss zum Gedächtniss,* 1856

When you can measure what you are speaking about, and express it in numbers, you know something about it; but when you cannot measure it, when you cannot express it in numbers, your knowledge is of a meagre and unsatisfactory kind: it may be the beginning of knowledge, but you have scarcely, in your thoughts, advanced to the stage of *science,* whatever the matter may be.

—WILLIAM THOMSON, LORD KELVIN, lecture, "Electrical Units of Measurement," 3 May 1883

If you know a thing only qualitatively, you know it no more than vaguely. If you know it quantitatively—grasping some numerical measure that distinguishes it from an infinite number of other possibilities—you are beginning to know it deeply. You comprehend some of its beauty and you gain access to its power and the understanding it provides. Being afraid of quantification is tantamount to disenfranchising yourself.

—CARL SAGAN, *Billions and Billions,* 1997

The knowledge of mathematical things is almost innate in us.... This is the easiest of sciences, a fact which is obvious in that no one's brain rejects it; for laymen and people who are utterly illiterate know how to count and reckon.

—ROGER BACON, *Opus Majus,* 1267

The theory of probabilities is at bottom nothing but common sense reduced to calculus.

—PIERRE SIMON DE LAPLACE, *Théorie Analytique des Probabilités,* vol. 7 of *Oeuvres,* 1812-20

If a man's wit be wandering, let him study the mathematics; for in demonstrations, if his wit be called away [ever] so little, he must begin again.

—FRANCIS BACON, *Essays,* 1625

I like mathematics because it is not human and has nothing particular to do with this planet or with the whole accidental universe—because, like Spinoza's God, it won't love us in return.

—BERTRAND RUSSELL, letter, March 1912

Politics is for the present, but an equation is something for eternity.

—ALBERT EINSTEIN, in Stephen Hawking,
A Brief History of Time, 1988

Nothing makes men more gentle than the cultivation of that heavenly philosophy [mathematics]. But, dear God, how rarely is this gentleness a quality of theologians! And how desirable it would be in this century if all theologians were mathematicians, that is, gentle and manageable men!

—PITISCUS, *Trigonometria,* 1612

So-called professional mathematicians have, in their reliance on the relative incapacity of the rest of mankind, acquired for themselves a reputation for profundity very similar to the reputation for sanctity possessed by theologians.

—G. C. LICHTENBERG, *Aphorisms*, written 1765-99

In many ways, the mathematical quest to understand infinity and higher-dimensional magic squares [number grids arranged in specific, symmetrical patterns] parallels mystical attempts to understand God. Both religion and mathematics attempt to express relationships between humans, the universe, and infinity. Both have arcane symbols and rituals and impenetrable language. Both exercise the deep recesses of our minds and stimulate our imagination. Mathematicians, like priests, seek ideal, immutable, nonmaterial truths and then often try to apply these truths in the real world.

—CLIFFORD A. PICKOVER, *The Zen of Magic Squares, Circles, and Stars*, 2002

When one sees a mathematical truth, one's consciousness breaks through into this world of ideas.... One may take the view that in such cases the mathematicians have stumbled upon works of God.

—ROGER PENROSE, *The Emperor's New Mind,* 1991

The mathematical phenomenon always develops out of simple arithmetic, so useful in everyday life, out of numbers, those weapons of the gods: the gods are there, behind the wall, at play with numbers.

—LE CORBUSIER, *Le Modulor,* 1948

Number is the within of all things.

—PYTHAGORAS (ca. 580-ca. 500 B.C.)

I have often admired the mystical way of Pythagoras, and the secret magic of numbers.

—Thomas Browne, *Religio Medici*, 1643

The science of pure mathematics, in its modern developments, may claim to be the most original creation of the human spirit.

—Alfred North Whitehead,
Science and the Modern World, 1925

God made integers, all else is the work of man.

—Leopold Kronecker (1823-91), mathematician,
Jahresberichte der Deutschen Mathematiker Vereinigung

From the intrinsic evidence of his creation, the Great Architect of the Universe now begins to appear as a pure mathematician.

—JAMES HOPWOOD JEANS,
The Mysterious Universe, 1930

I do not know if God is a mathematician, but mathematics is the loom upon which God weaves the fabric of the universe.

—CLIFFORD A. PICKOVER, *The Loom of God,* 1997

When Mr. Johnson felt his fancy, or felt he fancied it, disordered, his constant recurrence was to the study of arithmetic.

—HESTER PIOZZI, *Anecdeotes of
Samuel Johnson,* 1786

Philosophy is written in this grand book—I mean the universe—which stands continually open to our gaze, but it cannot be understood unless one first learns to comprehend the language and interpret the characters in which it is written. It is written in the language of mathematics, and its characters are triangles, circles, and other geometrical figures, without which it is humanly impossible to understand a single word of it.

—GALILEO GALILEI, *Il Saggiatore,* 1623

In Geometry (which is the only science that it hath pleased God hitherto to bestow on mankind) men begin at settling the significations of their words; which...they call Definitions.

—THOMAS HOBBES, *Leviathan,* 1651

Mathematics…would certainly not have come into existence if one had known from the beginning that there was in nature no exactly straight line, no actual circle, no absolute magnitude.

—FRIEDRICH NIETZSCHE,
Human, All Too Human, 1878

The universe is asymmetric and I am persuaded that life, as it is known to us, is a direct result of the asymmetry of the universe or of its indirect consequences. The universe is asymmetric.

—LOUIS PASTEUR, *Comptes Rendus de l'Académie des Sciences*, 1 June 1874

If the cosmos were suddenly frozen, and all movement ceased, a survey of its structure would not reveal a random distribution of parts. Simple geometrical patterns, for example, would be found in profusion—from the spirals of galaxies to the hexagonal shapes of snow crystals. Set the clockwork going, and its parts move rhythmically to laws that often can be expressed by equations of surprising simplicity. And there is no logical or a priori reason why these things should be so.

—MARTIN GARDNER, *Order and Surprise,* 1985

The harmony of the world is made manifest in Form and Number, and the heart and soul and all the poetry of Natural Philosophy are embodied in the concept of mathematical beauty.

—D'ARCY WENTWORTH THOMPSON, zoologist,
On Growth and Form, 1917

A mathematician, like a painter or a poet, is a maker of patterns. If his patterns are more permanent than theirs, it is because they are made with *ideas....* The mathematician's patterns, like the painter's or poet's, must be *beautiful*; the ideas, like the colours or the words, must fit together in a harmonious way.

—GODFREY HAROLD HARDY (1877-1947),
A Mathematician's Apology

Mathematics, rightly viewed, possesses not only truth, but supreme beauty—a beauty cold and austere, like that of sculpture, without appeal to any part of our weaker nature, without the gorgeous trappings of painting or music, yet sublimely pure, and capable of a stern perfection such as only the greatest art can show.

—BERTRAND RUSSELL,
The Study of Mathematics, 1902

Physics tries to discover the pattern of events which controls the phenomena we observe. But we can never know what this pattern means or how it originates; and even if some superior intelligence were to tell us, we should find the explanation unintelligible.

—JAMES HOPWOOD JEANS,
Physics and Philosophy, 1942

As far as the laws of mathematics refer to reality, they are not certain, and as far as they are certain, they do not refer to reality.

—ALBERT EINSTEIN, in Fritjof Capra,
The Tao of Physics, 1975

HEISENBERG'S UNCERTAINTY PRINCIPLE: The act of measurement affects whatever is being measured so that reality can never be apprehended precisely.

—WERNER HEISENBERG, 1927

Mathematics alone make us feel the limits of our intelligence. For we can always suppose in the case of an experiment that it is inexplicable because we don't happen to have all the data. In mathematics we have all the data...and yet we don't understand. We always come back to the contemplation of our human wretchedness. What force is in relation to our will, the impenetrable opacity of mathematics is in relation to our intelligence.

—SIMONE WEIL, *Notebooks*, 1952-55

Mathematics may be defined as the subject in which we never know what we are talking about, nor whether what we are saying is true.

—BERTRAND RUSSELL, *Mysticism and Logic*, 1917

The miracle of the appropriateness of the language of mathematics for the formulation of the laws of physics is a wonderful gift which we neither understand nor deserve. We should be grateful for it and hope that it will remain valid in future research and that it will extend, for better or for worse, to our pleasure even though perhaps also to our bafflement, to wide branches of learning.

—EUGENE P. WIGNER, *Communications in Pure and Applied Mathematics,* 1960

Concern for man himself and his fate must always form the chief interest of all technical endeavors, concern for the great unsolved problems of the organization of labor and the distribution of goods—in order that the creations of our mind shall be a blessing and not a curse to mankind. Never forget this in the midst of your diagrams and equations.

—ALBERT EINSTEIN, address at California Institute of Technology, 1931

Wonder, the Seed of Science

Men love to wonder, and that is the seed of our science.

— RALPH WALDO EMERSON, *Society and Solitude,* 1870

Curiosity is one of the most permanent and certain characteristics of a vigorous intellect.

— SAMUEL JOHNSON, in *The Rambler,* 12 March 1751

Everything in science depends on what one calls an aperçu, on becoming aware of what is at the bottom of the phenomena. Such becoming aware is infinitely fertile.

—JOHANN WOLFGANG VON GOETHE,
Galileo Galilei, 1810

It is his intuition, his mystical insight into the nature of things, rather than his reasoning which makes a great scientist.

—KARL POPPER,
The Open Society and Its Enemies, 1945

Every genuine scientist must be finally a meta-physician.

—GEORGE BERNARD SHAW, *Back to Methuselah,* 1921

For every man the world is as fresh as it was at the first day, and as full of untold novelties for him who has the eyes to see them.

—T. H. HUXLEY, *A Liberal Education*, 1868

For me chemistry represented an indefinite cloud of future potentialities which enveloped my life to come in black volutes torn by fiery flashes, like those which had hidden Mount Sinai. Like Moses, from that cloud I expected my law, the principle of order in me, around me, and in the world.... I would watch the buds swell in spring, the mica glint in the granite, my own hands, and I would say to myself: "I will understand this, too, I will understand everything."

—PRIMO LEVI, *The Periodic Table*, 1975

We cannot in any better manner glorify the Lord and Creator of the universe than that in all things, how small soever they appear to our naked eyes, but which have yet received the gift of life and power of increase, we contemplate the display of his omnificence and perfections with the utmost admiration.

—Anton van Leeuwenhoek (1632–1723), microscopy pioneer, *The Select Works of Anthony van Leeuwenhoek,* 1798

Although we are mere sojourners on the surface of the planet, chained to a mere point in space, enduring but for a moment of time, the human mind is not only enabled to number worlds beyond the unassisted ken of mortal eye, but to trace the events of indefinite ages before the creation of our race, and is not even withheld from penetrating into the dark secrets of the ocean, or the interior of the solid globe; free, like the spirit which the poet described as animating the universe.

—Charles Lyell, *Principles of Geology,* 1830

I ask you to look both ways. For the road to a knowledge of the stars leads through the atom; and important knowledge of the atom has been reached through the stars.

—Arthur Stanley Eddington, *Stars and Atoms,* 1928

I am standing on the threshold about to enter a room. It is a complicated business. In the first place I must shove against an atmosphere pressing with a force of fourteen pounds on every square inch of my body. I must make sure of landing on a plank travelling at twenty miles a second round the sun—a fraction of a second too early or too late, the plank would be miles away. I must do this whilst hanging from a round planet, head outward into space, and with a wind of aether blowing at no one knows how many miles a second through every interstice of my body.

—Arthur Stanley Eddington,
The Nature of the Physical World, 1928

Rotational motion seems to be a characteristic of most of the structures in the universe, from neutrinos to galaxies. Our earth rotates on its axis... [and, within the atom,] electrons rotate about the nucleus at speeds of from one per cent up to more than ten per cent of the speed of light, thereby giving a kind of solidity to the sphere of empty space in which they move.

—KENNETH W. FORD, *The World of Elementary Particles*, 1958

Viewed from the distance of the moon, the astonishing thing about the earth... is that it is alive.... Aloft, floating free beneath the moist, gleaming membrane of bright blue sky, is the rising earth, the only exuberant thing in this part of the cosmos.... It has the organized, self-contained look of a live creature, full of information, marvelously skilled in handling the sun.

—LEWIS THOMAS, *The Lives of a Cell,* 1974

How inappropriate to call this planet Earth when it is clearly Ocean.

—ARTHUR C. CLARKE, in *Nature*, 8 March 1990

Given for one instant an intelligence which could comprehend all the forces by which nature is animated and the respective positions of the beings which compose it, if moreover this intelligence were vast enough to submit these data to analysis, it would embrace in the same formula both the movements of the largest bodies in the universe and those of the lightest atom; to it nothing would be uncertain, and the future as the past would be present to its eyes.

—PIERRE SIMON DE LAPLACE, *Théorie Analytique des Probabilités*, vol. 7 of *Oeuvres*, 1812-20

The distinction between past, present and future is only an illusion, however persistent.

—ALBERT EINSTEIN, letter, 21 March 1955

Life is a wave, which in no two consecutive moments of its existence is composed of the same particles.

—JOHN TYNDALL (1820-93), *Fragments of Science*

The world we live in is but thickened light.

—RALPH WALDO EMERSON, *The Scholar,* 1883

The changing of bodies into light, and light into bodies, is very comfortable to the course of Nature, which seems delighted with transmutations.

—ISAAC NEWTON, *Opticks,* 1730

At a second split so fine that no clock could measure it, the entire observable universe is compressed within the wavelike blur described by the uncertainty principle, so tiny and compact that it could pass through the eye of a needle. Not just this room, or the earth, or the solar system, but *the entire universe* is squeezed into a dense dot of pure energy. And then comes the explosion.... It's an amazing picture, of pure and incredibly energetic light being transformed into matter, and leaving its vestiges behind.

—Owen Gingerich, in Roland Mushat Frye, ed., *Is God a Creationist?*, 1983

The matter of the universe consists largely of hydrogen. What would seem more logical than to look at this hydrogen as the residue of an explosion that took place at temperatures of more than 10^{28} degrees. In the consequent explosion matter formed and we got hydrogen atoms.

—Harald Fritzsch, *The Creation of Matter*, 1984

The uniformity of the earth's life, more astonishing than its diversity, is accountable by the high probability that we derived, originally, from some single cell, fertilized in a bolt of lightning as the earth cooled.

—LEWIS THOMAS, *The Lives of a Cell,* 1974

Would it be too bold to imagine, that in the great length of time, since the earth began to exist, perhaps millions of ages before the commencement of the history of mankind, would it be too bold to imagine, that all warm-blooded animals have arisen from one living filament which the Great First Cause endued with animality...and thus possessing the faculty of continuing to improve by its own inherent activity, and of delivering down those improvements by generation to its posterity, world without end!

—ERASMUS DARWIN, *Zoonomia,* 1794

From the war of nature, from famine and death, the most exalted object which we are capable of conceiving, namely, the production of the higher animals, directly follows. There is grandeur in this view of life, with its several powers, having been breathed into a few forms or into one; and that, whilst this planet has gone cycling on according to the fixed law of gravity, from so simple a beginning endless forms most beautiful and most wonderful have been, and are being, evolved.

—CHARLES DARWIN, *On the Origin of Species*, 1859

I was conscious of this vanished being and myself as part of an unbroken stream of consciousness.... With an imaginative effort it is possible to see the eternal present in which all days, all the seasons of the plain, stand in enduring unity.

—JACQUETTA HAWKES, on discovering a Neanderthal skeleton, in *New York Times Biographical Service*, 21 March 1996

It may be said that, so far from having a materialistic tendency, the supposed introduction into the earth at successive geological periods of life—sensation, instinct, the intelligence of the higher mammalia bordering on reason, and lastly, the improvable reason of Man himself—presents us with a picture of the ever-increasing dominion of mind over matter.

—CHARLES LYELL, *The Geological Evidences of the Antiquity of Man,* 1863

Today there is a wide measure of agreement, which on the physical side of science approaches almost to unanimity, that the stream of knowledge is heading toward a nonmechanical reality; the universe begins to look more like a great thought than like a great machine. Mind no longer appears as an accidental intruder into the realm of matter; we are beginning to suspect that we ought rather to hail it as the creator and governor of the realm of matter.

—JAMES HOPWOOD JEANS (1877-1946), in Joyce Carol Oates, "New Heaven and Earth," 1972

The universe is one of God's thoughts.

—FRIEDRICH VON SCHILLER, *Essays*, 1884

Whence is it that Nature does nothing in vain: and whence arises all that order and beauty which we see in the world?...does it not appear from phenomena that there is a Being incorporeal, living, intelligent, omnipresent, who in infinite space, as it were in his Sensory, sees the things themselves intimately, and thoroughly perceives them, and comprehends them wholly.

—ISAAC NEWTON, *Opticks*, 1730

Is the universe a great mechanism, a great computation, a great symmetry, a great accident or a great thought?

—JOHN D. BARROW, astronomer,
in *New York Times*, 30 December 1997

Perhaps the immense Milky Way which on clear nights we behold stretching across the heavens, this vast encircling ring in which our planetary system is itself but a molecule, is in turn but a cell in the Universe, in the Body of God.

—Miguel de Unamuno, *Tragic Sense of Life,* 1913

Now, my own suspicion is that the universe is not only queerer than we suppose, but queerer than we *can* suppose. I have read and heard many attempts at a systematic account of it, from materialism and theosophy to the Christian system or that of Kant, and I have always felt that they were much too simple. I suspect that there are more things in heaven and earth than are dreamed of, or can be dreamed of, in any philosophy. That is the reason why I have no philosophy myself, and must be my excuse for dreaming.

—J. B. S. Haldane, *Possible Worlds and Other Papers,* 1927

Labors of the Laboratory

The brightest flashes in the world of thought are incomplete until they have been proved to have their counterparts in the world of fact.

—JOHN TYNDALL (1820-93), *Fragments of Science*

Ideas won't keep. Something must be done about them.

—ALFRED NORTH WHITEHEAD, *Dialogues,* 1954

When curiosity turns to serious matters, it's called research.

—MARIE VON EBNER-ESCHENBACH,
Aphorisms, 1880-1905

Basic research is what I am doing when I don't know what I am doing.

—WERNER VON BRAUN (1912-77), in R. L. Weber,
A Random Walk in Science, 1973

What you need at the outset [of basic research] is a high degree of uncertainty; otherwise it isn't likely to be an important problem. You start with an incomplete roster of facts, characterized by their ambiguity; often the problem consists of discovering the connections between unrelated pieces of information. You must plan experiments on the basis of probability, even bare possibility, rather than certainty.

—LEWIS THOMAS, *The Lives of a Cell*, 1974

When the great innovation appears, it will almost certainly be in a muddled, incomplete and confusing form. To the discoverer himself it will be only half-understood; to everybody else it will be a mystery. For any speculation which does not at first glance look crazy, there is no hope.

—WERNER HEISENBERG, *Physics and Beyond,* 1971

The great thinkers from whom we derive inspiration enjoyed insights beyond their own systems. They made statements hard to reconcile with the neat little ways of thought which we pin on to their names.

—ALFRED NORTH WHITEHEAD, *Modes of Thought,* 1938

The secret of all those who make discoveries is that they regard nothing as impossible.

—JUSTUS VON LIEBIG (1803-73),
German chemist, in Emerson's journal

Nothing is too wonderful to be true, if it be consistent with the laws of nature, and in such things as these, experiment is the best test of such consistency.

—MICHAEL FARADAY, diary, 19 March 1849

If you have a scientific imagination, you can think of all sorts of things that might be true, and that's the essence of science. You first think of something that might be true—then you look to see if it is, and generally it isn't.

—BERTRAND RUSSELL, television interview, 1959

The first precept was never to accept a thing as true until I knew it as such without a single doubt.

—RENÉ DESCARTES, *Le Discours de la Méthode,* 1637

I frame no hypotheses; for whatever is not deduced from the phenomena is to be called an hypothesis; and hypotheses, whether metaphysical or physical, whether of occult qualities or mechanical, have no place in experimental philosophy.

—Isaac Newton, letter to Robert Hooke,
5 February 1675/76

It is a capital mistake to theorize before one has data.

—Arthur Conan Doyle,
"A Scandal in Bohemia," 1891

The moment a person forms a theory, his imagination sees in every object only the traits which favor that theory.

—Thomas Jefferson, letter, 20 September 1787

If someone points out to you that your pet theory of the universe is in disagreement with Maxwell's equations—then so much the worse for Maxwell's equations. If it is found to be contradicted by observation—well, these experimentalists do bungle things sometimes. But if your theory is found to be against the second law of thermodynamics I can give you no hope; there is nothing for it but to collapse in deepest humiliation.

—ARTHUR STANLEY EDDINGTON, *The Nature of the Physical World,* 1928

The great tragedy of Science—the slaying of a beautiful hypothesis by an ugly fact.

—T. H. HUXLEY, "Biogenesis and Abiogenesis," 1870

It is a good morning exercise for a research scientist to discard a pet hypothesis every day before breakfast. It keeps him young.

—Konrad Lorenz, zoologist, *On Aggression,* 1963

I shall certainly admit a system as empirical or scientific only if it is capable of being *tested* by experience. These considerations suggest that not the *verifiability* but the *falsifiability* of a system is to be taken as a criterion of demarcation.... *It must be possible for an empirical scientific system to be refuted by experience.*

—Karl Popper, *The Logic of Scientific Discovery,* 1934

It is a test of true theories not only to account for but to predict phenomena.

—William Whewell, *Philosophy of the Inductive Sciences,* 1840

The test of science is predictability.

—ARTHUR M. SCHLESINGER JR., in *Atlantic*, July 1963

Science is feasible when the variables are few and can be enumerated; when their combinations are distinct and clear. We are tending toward the condition of science and aspiring to do it. The artist works out his own formulas; the interest of science lies in the art of making science.

—PAUL VALÉRY, *Moralités*, 1932

Science is nothing but trained and organized common sense, differing from the latter only as a veteran may differ from a raw recruit: and its methods differ from those of common sense only as far as the guardsman's cut and thrust differ from the manner in which a savage wields his club.

—T. H. HUXLEY, "The Method of Zadig," 1893-94

Every experiment is like a weapon which must be used in its particular way—a spear to thrust, a club to strike. Experimenting requires a man who knows when to thrust and when to strike, each according to need and fashion.

—PARACELSUS, *Surgeon's Book,* 1605

MURPHY'S LAW: If anything can go wrong, it will.

—EDWARD A. MURPHY JR., flight engineer,
Edwards Air Force Base, 1949

I love fools' experiments. I am always making them.

—CHARLES DARWIN, in Francis Darwin,
Life and Letters of Charles Darwin, 1887

One of the favourite maxims of my father was the distinction between the two sorts of truths, profound truths recognized by the fact that the opposite is also a profound truth, in contrast to trivialities where opposites are obviously absurd.

—NIELS BOHR (1885–1962), in S. Rozental,
Niels Bohr, 1967

Two things are identical if one can be substituted for the other without affecting the truth.

—GOTTFRIED WILHELM LEIBNIZ,
"Table de Définitions," 1704

It belongs to the self-respect of intellect to pursue every tangle of thought to its final unravelment.

—ALFRED NORTH WHITEHEAD,
Science and the Modern World, 1925

All thinking is...a state of unrest tending towards equilibrium.

—SAMUEL BUTLER (1835-1902), *Notebooks*

There is no expedient to which a man will not go to avoid the real labor of thinking.

—THOMAS ALVA EDISON (1847-1931),
motto in his laboratories

We haven't got the money, so we've got to think!

—ERNEST RUTHERFORD, in *Bulletin of the
Institute of Physics,* 1962

To be fruitful in invention, it is indispensable to have a *habit* of observation and reflection.

—ABRAHAM LINCOLN, lecture, 11 February 1859

The first rule of intelligent tinkering is to save all the parts.

—PAUL RALPH EHRLICH, biologist,
in *Saturday Review*, 5 June 1971

Discovery consists of seeing what everybody has seen and thinking what nobody has thought.

—ALBERT VON SZENT-GYÖRGYI (1893–1986),
biochemist who discovered vitamin C

Familiar things happen, and mankind does not bother about them. It requires a very unusual mind to undertake the analysis of the obvious.

—ALFRED NORTH WHITEHEAD,
Science and the Modern World, 1925

Invention, strictly speaking, is little more than a new combination of those images which have been previously gathered and deposited in the memory: nothing can come of nothing: he who has laid up no materials can produce no combinations.

—Joshua Reynolds,
"Discourse Two," 11 December 1769

Where observation is concerned, chance favours only the prepared mind.

—Louis Pasteur, lecture at
University of Lille, 7 December 1854

Invention presupposes an extensive contemplation of things on one's own account; one must see for oneself more than let oneself be told.

—G. C. Lichtenberg, *Aphorisms,* written 1765-99

Inventing is a combination of brains and materials. The more brains you use, the less material you need.

—CHARLES F. KETTERING (1876–1958),
electrical engineer and inventor

Very often it happens that a discovery is made whilst working upon quite another problem.

—THOMAS ALVA EDISON, diary, 1922

The intellect has little to do on the road to discovery. There comes a leap in consciousness, call it intuition or what you will, and the solution comes to you and you don't know how or why.

—ALBERT EINSTEIN

The moment of truth, the sudden emergence of a new insight, is an act of intuition. Such intuitions give the appearance of miraculous flushes, or short-circuits of reasoning. In fact they may be likened to an immersed chain, of which only the beginning and the end are visible above the surface of consciousness. The diver vanishes at one end of the chain and comes up at the other end, guided by invisible links.

—Arthur Koestler, *The Act of Creation*, 1964

Finally, two days ago I succeeded, not on account of my painful efforts, but by the Grace of God. Like a sudden flash of lightning, the riddle happened to be solved. I myself cannot say what was the conducting thread which connected what I previously knew with what made my success possible.

—Carl Friedrich Gauss (1777-1855),
German mathematician and astronomer

The tendency to celebrate, on making a fine discovery, is fairly universal among scientists, but most of the mathematicians I know believe that the kingdom of God is within themselves, and therefore do something which pleases the inner man when they complete a good piece of research. Those who like cigars buy themselves an exceptionally good cigar, and so on, bribing the inner consciousness, or the subconscious, whatever it may be, to produce more good results. And mathematicians were doing this a long time before Skinner evolved his theories of reinforcement.

—DAN PEDOE, *Geometry and the Visual Arts*, 1976

The Human Impact of Science

This is the patent age of new inventions
For killing bodies and for saving souls,
All propagated with the best intentions.

—LORD BYRON, *Don Juan,* 1819-24

What hath God wrought?

—SAMUEL F. B. MORSE,
first telegraph message, 24 May 1844

In my own time there have been inventions of this sort, transparent windows...tubes for diffusing warmth equally through all parts of a building... short-hand, which has been carried to such a perfection that a writer can keep pace with the most rapid speaker. But the inventing of such things is drudgery for the lowest slaves.

—SENECA THE YOUNGER (ca. 5 B.C.–A.D. 65),
Epistulae ad Lucilium

It is well to observe the force and virtue and consequence of discoveries, and these are to be seen nowhere more conspicuously than in those three which were unknown to the ancients, and of which the origins, though recent, are obscure and inglorious; namely, printing, gunpowder, and the mariner's needle [compass]...these three have changed the whole face and state of things throughout the world.

—FRANCIS BACON, *Novum Organum*, 1620

Man is a tool-using animal.... Without tools he is nothing, with tools he is all.

—THOMAS CARLYLE, *Sartor Resartus,* 1833-34

Is it fact, or have I dreamt it—that, by means of electricity, the world of matter has become a great nerve, vibrating thousands of miles in a breathless point of time.

—NATHANIEL HAWTHORNE,
The House of the Seven Gables, 1851

Man is a shrewd inventor, and is ever taking the hint of a new machine from his own structure, adapting some secret of his own anatomy in iron, wood, and leather, to some required function in the work of the world.

—RALPH WALDO EMERSON, *English Traits,* 1856

Blessed be the inventor of photography! I set him above even the inventor of chloroform! It has given more positive pleasure to poor suffering humanity than anything else that has "cast up" in my time or is like to—this art by which even the "poor" can possess themselves of tolerable likenesses of their absent dear ones. And mustn't it be acting favourably on the morality of the country?

—JANE WELSH CARLYLE, letter, 21 October 1859

The machine unmakes the man. Now that the machine is so perfect, the engineer is nobody. Every new step in improving the engine restricts one more act of the engineer—unteaches him. Once it took Archimedes; now it only needs a fireman, and a boy to know the coppers, to pull up the handles or mind the water tank. But when the engine breaks, they can do nothing.

—RALPH WALDO EMERSON, *Society and Solitude,* 1860

Furnished as all Europe now is with Academies of Science, with nice instruments and the spirit of experiment, the progress of human knowledge will be rapid and discoveries made of which we have at present no conception. I begin to be almost sorry I was born so soon, since I cannot have the happiness of knowing what will be known a hundred years hence.

—Benjamin Franklin, letter, 27 July 1783

I firmly believe that before many centuries more, science will be the master of man. The engines he will have invented will be beyond his strength to control. Some day science may have the existence of mankind in its power, and the human race commit suicide by blowing up the world.

—Henry Brooks Adams,
letter to his brother, 11 April 1862

Mr. Watson, come here, I want to see you.

—ALEXANDER GRAHAM BELL,
first telephone message, 10 March 1876

When at last this little instrument appeared, consisting, as it does, of parts every one of which is familiar to us, and capable of being put together by an amateur, the disappointment arising from its humble appearance was only partially relieved on finding that it was really able to talk.

—JAMES CLERK MAXWELL, *The Telephone*, 1878

My [explosives] factories may make an end of war sooner than your congresses. The day when two army corps can annihilate each other in one second, all civilized nations, it is to be hoped, will recoil from war and discharge their troops.

—ALFRED NOBEL (1833-96), in Bertha von Suttner,
Memoiren, 1909

SUCCESS FOUR FLIGHTS THURSDAY MORNING ALL
AGAINST TWENTY ONE MILE WIND STARTED FROM LEVEL
WITH ENGINE POWER ALONE SPEED THROUGH AIR
THIRTY ONE MILES LONGEST FIFTY SEVEN SECOND
INFORM PRESS HOME CHRISTMAS

> —WILBUR AND ORVILLE WRIGHT,
> telegram from Kitty Hawk, 17 December 1903

It [deflection of an alpha particle beam by metal foil] was quite the most incredible event that has ever happened to me in my life. It was almost as incredible as if you fired a 15-inch shell at a piece of tissue paper and it came back and hit you.

> —ERNEST RUTHERFORD, winner of Nobel prize
> for chemistry in 1908

When Rutherford was done with the atom all the solidity was pretty well knocked out of it.

> —STEPHEN LEACOCK, *The Boy I Left Behind Me,* 1947

A house is a machine for living in.

—Le Corbusier, *Vers une Architecture*, 1923

In the past human life was lived in a bullock cart; in the future it will be lived in an aeroplane; and the change of speed amounts to a difference in quality.

—Alfred North Whitehead,
Science and the Modern World, 1925

I saw a fleet of fishing boats.... I flew down almost touching the craft and yelled at them, asking if I was on the right road to Ireland.

They just stared. Maybe they didn't hear me. Maybe I didn't hear them. Or maybe they thought I was just a crazy fool. An hour later I saw land.

—Charles A. Lindbergh,
in *New York Times*, 23 May 1927

The clock, not the steam engine, is the key-machine of the modern industrial age.

—LEWIS MUMFORD, *Technics and Civilization*, 1934

Science, unguided by a higher abstract principle, freely hands over its secrets to a vastly developed and commercially inspired technology, and the latter, even less restrained by a supreme culture saving principle, with the means of science creates all the instruments of power demanded from it by the organization of Might.

—JOHAN HUIZINGA, *In the Shadow of Tomorrow*, 1936

The reason for so much bad science is not that talent is rare, not at all; what is rare is character.

—SIGMUND FREUD (1856-1939), in Joseph Wortis, *Fragments of an Analysis with Freud,* 1954

We are living now, not in the delicious intoxication induced by the early successes of science, but in a rather grisly morning-after, when it has become apparent that what triumphant science has done hitherto is to improve the means for achieving unimproved or actually deteriorated ends.

—ALDOUS HUXLEY, *Ends and Means,* 1937

Some recent work by E. Fermi and L. Szilard, which has been communicated to me in manuscript, leads me to expect that the element uranium may be turned into a new and important source of energy in the immediate future. Certain aspects of the situation which has arisen seem to call for watchfulness and, if necessary, quick action on the part of the Administration.

—ALBERT EINSTEIN, letter to Franklin D. Roosevelt, 2 August 1939

The latest refinements of science are linked with the cruelties of the Stone Age.

—WINSTON CHURCHILL,
speech, on the effects of war, 26 March 1942

The Italian Navigator has reached the new world.

—ARTHUR HOLLY COMPTON, coded message telephoned to National Defense Research Committee announcing that Enrico Fermi had produced the first controlled nuclear chain reaction, 2 December 1942

We knew the world would not be the same. A few people laughed, a few people cried. Most people were silent. I remembered the line from the Hindu scripture, the Bhagavad Gita.... "I am become Death, the destroyer of worlds." I suppose we all thought that, one way or another.

—J. ROBERT OPPENHEIMER, recalling the first atomic explosion in New Mexico on 16 July 1945

There was no sound of planes. The morning [of 6 August 1945] was still; the place was cool and pleasant.

Then a tremendous flash of light cut across the sky. Mr. Tanimoto has a distinct recollection that it traveled from east to west, from the city toward the hills. It seemed a sheet of sun. Both he and Mr. Matsuo reacted in terror.... Under what seemed to be a local dust cloud, the day grew darker and darker....

There, in the tin factory, in the first moment of the atomic age, a human being was crushed by books.

—JOHN HERSEY, *Hiroshima*, 1946

The unleashed power of the atom has changed everything save our modes of thinking and we thus drift toward unparalleled catastrophe.

—ALBERT EINSTEIN, telegram to prominent Americans, 24 May 1946

The degradation of the position of the scientist as independent worker and thinker to that of a morally irresponsible stooge in a science-factory has proceeded even more rapidly and devastatingly than I had expected.

—NORBERT WEINER, in *Bulletin of the Atomic Scientists*, 4 November 1948

When you see something that is technically sweet, you go ahead and do it and you argue about what to do about it only after you have had your technical success. That is the way it was with the atomic bomb.

—J. ROBERT OPPENHEIMER, in *In the Matter of J. Robert Oppenheimer, USAEC Transcript of Hearing Before Personnel Security Board,* 1954

I am sorry to say that there is too much point to the wisecrack that life is extinct on other planets because their scientists were more advanced than ours.

—JOHN F. KENNEDY, speech, 11 December 1959

The pursuit of the good and evil are now linked in astronomy as in almost all science.... The fate of human civilization will depend on whether the rockets of the future carry the astronomer's telescope or a hydrogen bomb.

—BERNARD LOVELL,
The Individual and the Universe, 1959

The means by which we live have outdistanced the ends for which we live. Our scientific power has outrun our spiritual power. We have guided missiles and misguided men.

—MARTIN LUTHER KING JR., *Strength to Love*, 1963

It was through the Second World War that most of us suddenly appreciated for the first time the power of man's concentrated efforts to understand and control the forces of nature. We were appalled by what we saw.

—Vannevar Bush, *Science Is Not Enough*, 1967

I have seen the science I worshipped, and the aircraft I loved, destroying the civilization I expected them to serve.... To progress, even to survive, we must learn to apply the truths of God to the direction of our science.

—Charles A. Lindbergh, in *Time*, 26 May 1967

No science is immune to the infection of politics and the corruption of power.

—Jacob Bronowski, in *Encounter*, July 1971

Every day I saw the huge material, intellectual and nervous resources of thousands of people being poured into the creation of a means of total destruction, something capable of annihilating all human civilization. I noticed that the control levers were in the hands of people who, though talented in their own ways, were cynical.

—ANDREI SAKHAROV, *Sakharov Speaks*, 1974

The future of humanity is uncertain, even in the most prosperous countries, and the quality of life deteriorates; and yet I believe that what is being discovered about the infinitely large and infinitely small is sufficient to absolve this end of the century and millennium. What a very few are acquiring in knowledge of the physical world will perhaps cause this period not to be judged as a pure return of barbarism.

—PRIMO LEVI, *Other People's Trades*, 1985

Plumbing the Depths of Science

The sciences have developed in an order the reverse of what might have been expected. What was most remote from ourselves was first brought under the domain of law, and then, gradually, what was nearer: first the heavens, next the earth, then animal and vegetable life, then the human body, and last of all (as yet very imperfectly) the human mind.

—BERTRAND RUSSELL, *Religion and Science*, 1935

The matter of mind, in general, and of consciousness, in particular, allows humans to exercise, to the vanishing point, the desire for understanding and the appetite for wonderment at their own nature that Aristotle recognized as so distinctively human. What could be more difficult to know than to know how we know? What could be more dizzying than to realize that it is our having consciousness which makes possible and even inevitable our questions about consciousness?

—ANTONIO DAMASIO,
The Feeling of What Happens, 1999

What is it that breathes fire into the equations and makes a universe for them to describe?... Why does the universe go to all the bother of existing?... If we find the answer to that, it would be the ultimate triumph of human reason—for then we would know the mind of God.

—STEPHEN HAWKING, *A Brief History of Time,* 1988

Science is wonderfully equipped to answer the question "how?" but it gets terribly confused when you ask the question "why?"

—Erwin Chargaff, biochemist, in *Columbia Forum,* summer 1969

Science tries to answer the question: "How?" How do cells act in the body? How do you design an airplane that will fly faster than sound? How is a molecule of insulin constructed? Religion, by contrast, tries to answer the question: "Why?" Why was man created? Why ought I to tell the truth? Why must there be sorrow or pain or death? Science attempts to analyze how things and people and animals behave; it has no concern whether this behavior is good or bad, is purposeful or not. But religion is precisely the quest for such answers: whether an act is right or wrong, good or bad, and why.

—Warren Weaver, *Science and Imagination,* 1967

Science…takes no cognizance of the things that make life worth living, for the simple reason that beauty, love, and so on, are not measurable quantities, and science deals only with what can be measured.

—ALDOUS HUXLEY,
Do What You Will, 1929

The aim of science is not to open the door to infinite wisdom, but to set a limit to infinite error.

—BERTOLT BRECHT, *The Life of Galileo*, 1939

The empiricist view is so deep-seated in our way of looking at the human mind that it almost has the character of a superstition.

—NOAM CHOMSKY, in *Listener*, 30 May 1968

Traditional scientific method has always been at the very *best,* 20-20 hindsight. It's good for seeing where you've been. It's good for testing the truth of what you think you know, but it can't tell you where you *ought* to go.

—ROBERT M. PIRSIG, *Zen and the Art of Motorcycle Maintenance,* 1974

Vanity of science. Knowledge of physical science will not console me for ignorance of morality in time of affliction, but knowledge of morality will always console me for ignorance of physical science.

—BLAISE PASCAL, *Pensées,* 1670

Science, after all, is only an expression for our ignorance of our own ignorance.

—SAMUEL BUTLER (1835–1902), *Notebooks*

We need to have the spirit of science in international affairs, to make the conduct of international affairs the effort to find the right solution, the just solution of international problems, not the effort by each nation to get the better of other nations, to do harm to them when it is possible.

—LINUS PAULING, *No More War!*, 1958

Science and technology, and the various forms of art, all unite humanity in a single and interconnected system. As science progresses, the worldwide cooperation of scientists and technologists becomes more and more of a special and distinct intellectual community of friendship, in which, in place of antagonism, there is growing up a mutually advantageous sharing of work, a coordination of efforts, a common language for the exchange of information, and a solidarity, which are in many cases independent of the social and political differences of individual states.

—ZHORES MEDVEDEV, *The Medvedev Papers*, 1970

The delights of science and mathematics—their revelations of natural beauty and harmony, their visions of things to come, and the joy of discovery in itself, the light and shadow it casts on the mystery dance of mind and nature—are too profound, and too important, to be left to scientists and mathematicians alone. They belong to the cultural heritage of the entire world, and to know something about them is to be acquainted with the finest new achievements of the human mind.

—TIMOTHY FERRIS, ed., *The World Treasury of Physics, Astronomy, and Mathematics,* 1991

To a person uninstructed in natural history, his country or seaside stroll is a walk through a gallery filled with wonderful works of art, nine-tenths of which have their faces turned to the wall.

—T. H. HUXLEY, "On the Educational Value of the Natural History Sciences," 1854

Most of the fundamental ideas of science are essentially simple, and may, as a rule, be expressed in a language comprehensible to anyone.

—ALBERT EINSTEIN, with Leopold Infeld,
The Evolution of Physics, 1938

I was asked to address [a meeting of philosophers] on the interpretation of quantum theory. After my lecture, no one raised any objections or asked any embarrassing questions, but I must say this very fact proved a terrible disappointment to me. For those who are not shocked when they first come across quantum theory cannot possibly have understood it. Probably I spoke so badly that no one knew what I was talking about.

—NIELS BOHR (1885-1962), in Werner Heisenberg,
Physics and Beyond, 1971

I read with infinite pleasure Eddington's *Nature of the Physical World* which for 24 hours almost persuaded me that I had caught a glimpse of what the new physics was really about. It wasn't, of course, true; but the sensation, while it lasted, was charming.

—HAROLD LASKI, letter to Oliver Wendell Holmes,
30 November 1928

It is said that there are, besides Dr Einstein himself, only two men who can claim to have grasped the Theory in full. I cannot claim to be either of these.... The attempt to conceive Infinity had always been quite arduous enough for me. But to imagine the absence of it; to feel that perhaps we and all the stars beyond our ken are somehow cosily (though awfully) closed in by curtain curves beyond which is nothing; and to convince myself, by the way, that this exterior is not (in virtue of *being* nothing) something, and therefore...but I lose the thread.

—MAX BEERBOHM, *Mainly on the Air,* 1947

There was a young lady named Bright,
Whose speed was far faster than light;
She set out one day
In a relative way,
And returned on the previous night.

—A. H. REGINALD BULLER, mycologist, in *Punch,*
19 December 1923

When you are courting a nice girl an hour seems like a second. When you sit on a red-hot cinder a second seems like an hour. That's relativity.

—ALBERT EINSTEIN, in *News Chronicle,*
14 March 1949

Never express yourself more clearly than you think.

—NIELS BOHR (1885-1962), in Abraham Pais,
Einstein Lived Here, 1994

Einstein is loved because he is gentle, respected because he is wise. Relativity being not for most of us, we elevate its author to a position somewhere between Edison, who gave us a tangible gleam, and God, who gave us the difficult dark and the hope of penetrating it.

—E. B. WHITE, in *New Yorker,* 8 April 1933

You imagine that I look back on my life's work with calm satisfaction, but from nearby it looks quite different. There is not a single concept of which I am convinced it will stand firm, and I feel uncertain whether I am in general on the right track.

—ALBERT EINSTEIN, letter to
Maurice Solovine, 28 March 1949

The profound thinker always suspects that he is superficial.

—BENJAMIN DISRAELI, *Contarini Fleming,* 1832

Scientists all agree that somehow the simpler of two theories, each with the same explanatory and predictive power, has the better chance of being fruitful, but no one knows why. Maybe it's because the ultimate laws of nature are simple, but who can be positive there really are ultimate laws? Some physicists suspect there may be infinite levels of complexity. At each level the laws may get progressively simpler until suddenly the experimenters open a trap door and another complicated subbasement is discovered.

—MARTIN GARDNER, *The Colossal Book of Mathematics*, 2001

One does not, by knowing all the fundamental laws as we know them today, immediately obtain an understanding of anything much. It takes a while, and even then it is only partial. Nature, as a matter of fact, seems to be so designed that the most important things in the real world appear to be a kind of complicated accidental result of a lot of laws.

—RICHARD P. FEYNMAN,
The Character of Physical Law, 1965

To a very large extent we will have to rely on mathematical beauty and consistency to find the ultimate Theory of Everything. Nevertheless, I am confident we will discover it by the end of the 21st century and probably much sooner. I would take a bet at 50-50 odds that it will be within 20 years starting now.

—STEPHEN HAWKING, speech, 19 March 1998

Many of the things that the theory [of Everything] predicts unambiguously in principle could require intractable calculations. Part of the art of physics is to identify those things that can be calculated....

—JOHN SCHWARZ, "A Theory of Everything?," 1996

No *good* model ever accounted for *all* the facts, since some data was bound to be misleading if not plain wrong.

—JAMES D. WATSON, in Francis Crick,
What Mad Pursuit, 1988

In effect, we have redefined the task of science to be the discovery of laws that will enable us to predict events up to the limits set by the uncertainty principle.

—STEPHEN HAWKING, *A Brief History of Time*, 1988

We should like Nature to go no further; we should like it to be finite, like our mind; but this is to ignore the greatness and majesty of the Author of things.

—GOTTFRIED WILHELM LEIBNIZ, letter, 1715

For after all, what is man in nature? A nothing in respect of that which is infinite, an all in respect of nothing, a middle betwixt nothing and all.

—BLAISE PASCAL, *Pensées,* 1670

In my youth I regarded the universe as an open book, printed in the language of physical equations, whereas now it appears to me as a text written in invisible ink, of which in our rare moments of grace we are able to decipher a small fragment.

—ARTHUR KOESTLER, *Bricks to Babel,* 1980

I do not know what I may appear to the world; but to myself I seem to have been only like a boy playing on the seashore, and diverting myself in now and then finding a smoother pebble or a prettier shell than ordinary, whilst the great ocean of truth lay all undiscovered before me.

—ISAAC NEWTON (1642-1727), in David Brewster, ed.,
Memoirs of Newton, 1855

Vast is the field of Science. The more a man knows, the more he will find he has to know.

—SAMUEL RICHARDSON,
Sir Charles Grandison, 1753-54

A man ceases to be a beginner in any given science and becomes a master in that science when he has learned that...he is going to be a beginner all his life.

—R. G. COLLINGWOOD, *The New Leviathan*, 1942